Put Ted the tractor
driver in the picture.

The cow shed

Ted is looking after the cows.
Where could Daisy the cow go?

Put a bull inside
the shed.

This little rabbit
needs some friends.

Usborne Farmyard Tales
Sticker Book

Contents

Illustrated by
Stephen Cartwright

There is a little yellow duck to find in every picture.

Apple Tree Farm

Mr. and Mrs. Boot live here with their children, Poppy and Sam. Can you add them to the picture?

Stick Whiskers the cat in the picture.

Find a place for Clucky the hen.

Stick Poppy and
Sam in the picture.

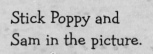

Ted's tractor

Ted is fixing the tractor. He needs his tools, and some help from Poppy and Sam.

Put Gertie the goat in this field.

Put Rusty the dog in the picture.

Can you put some sacks of animal food in the trailer?

Dolly the horse

Dolly the horse and Penny the pony are friends.
Can you add them to the picture?

Find a place for
Poppy and Sam.

Apple Tree Farm

Birds

Duck

Balloon

Hens

Ball

Kittens

Whiskers the cat

Mrs. Boot hanging out the clothes

Clothes basket

Ted in his tractor

Mr. Boot sweeping

Clucky the hen

Poppy riding her bike

Rusty the dog and Sam

The cow shed

Bull

Cow

Rabbits

Cows

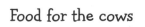

Food for the cows

Poppy

Sam

Daisy the cow

Rusty the dog

Ted's tractor

Whiskers the cat

Frogs

Gertie the goat

Shovel

Animal food

Hens

Clucky the hen

Mice

Ted's tools

Ted's toolbox

Bird

Rope

Paint

Sam

Rusty the dog

Poppy

Dolly the horse

Bird

Rusty the dog

Ducks

Dolly the horse

Poppy

Butterflies

Penny the pony

Sam

The pig pen

Curly the pig

Mother pig

Pigs

Mrs. Boot

Snail

Poppy

Sam

The sheep field

Butterfly

Patch the sheepdog

Food for the sheep

Mrs. Boot

Ted

Sheep

Woolly the sheep

Sam

Boat

Poppy

Rusty the dog

Frog

Ducks

The hen house

Trike

Whiskers the cat

Hen and chicks

Ted

Mouse

Hen food

Goose

Chicks

Hens

Mrs. Boot

Clucky the hen

Sam

Poppy

Rusty the dog

The orchard

Sam

Mrs. Boot

Rabbit

Squirrel

Whiskers the cat

Apples

Plant pots

Crow

Poppy

Ted

Rusty the dog

Vegetables

Basket

Watering can

Butterfly

Wheelbarrow

Hen and chick

Scarecrow

Clucky the hen

The barn

Bird

Cows

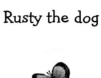

Rabbits

Rusty the dog

Butterfly

Curly the pig

Pigs

Woolly the sheep

Goose

Duck

Gertie the goat

Chicks

Clucky the hen

Ears the donkey

Whiskers the cat

Dolly the horse

The pig pen

Curly is the smallest pig on the farm.
Stick Curly and all the other pigs in the pen.

Where could the
mother pig go?

Stick Mrs. Boot
in the picture.

The sheep field

Woolly the sheep and her friends live here.
Can you put them in the field?

Find a place for Ted
and his wheelbarrow.

Add Patch the sheepdog
to the picture.

Poppy and Sam like
to play in this stream.

The hen house

The hens lay lots of eggs in the hen house.
Find a place for Mrs. Boot collecting the eggs.

Where could
Rusty the dog go?

Put Ted in
the picture.

These hens are hungry.
Can you give them
some food?

The orchard

The orchard is full of apple trees. Add Mrs. Boot and Ted picking apples to the picture.

The vegetable patch needs a scarecrow to scare away the crows.

14

Sam loves to swing
from the apple tree.

Put Poppy carrying
apples in the picture.

The barn

Can you make your own picture using the animal stickers?